James Gillray – the untold stories

Love, Intrigue & Chicanery

TONY ROTHWELL

*For my wife, Camilla, editor-in-chief, my family
and all those who encouraged me to write.*

Printed in the United States of America

ISBN 978-0-578-90824-3

Love, Intrigue & Chicanery

James Gillray
1756 - 1815
from a self-portrait

Introduction

*J*ames Gillray was a British caricaturist and printmaker active from 1779 to 1811. He became famous in his own lifetime for his unmerciful satires on politicians, high society and the Royal family during the scandal-rich Regency period, earning him the contemporary description of 'a caterpillar on the green leaf of reputation'. Today, he is arguably the most influential caricaturist the world has known.

How did my involvement with him begin? As a young man living in London in the 60's, I was riding the Underground going home to my bed-sit from work at Unilever when I noticed an advertisement for an exhibition of caricatures by a James Gillray at The Arts Council in St. James's Square. I didn't remember the name, but I recognised the illustration they used for the ad. It was *The Plumb-pudding in danger*, (see page 51), which I had copied by hand from a history textbook at Denstone College some 8 years before, being impressed by its graphic design. Already a cartoon nut, I visited the exhibition the very next day and was captivated by everything I saw. There and then I determined to turn London upside down, shake it, and see just how many Gillrays would fall out.

I had immediate success. It seems incredible now, but I was buying prints for just a few pounds. So started a lifetime of collecting and research into Gillray and his contemporaries like Rowlandson and Cruikshank, spending many hours in The Print Room at the British Museum on Saturdays and chasing down caricatures, not only in London, but all over the world. And my interest continues to this day sustained by Gillray's imagination, his understanding of human frailty and his wicked wit, added to his outstanding skill with the engraving tool and superb sense of composition.

But while he is credited with being the father of the political cartoon, he also dabbled in the world outside the high and mighty, satirizing everyday social situations from ideas often provided by friends. As I delved into his work, I became familiar with those prints also, some of which had no known background descriptions in either contemporary books or the British Museum's archives. I thought it would be fun to remedy that situation which was the inspiration for the stories in this book.

The first of them, 'Slippery Sam', is really an extension of this introduction - a glimpse into the world in which Gillray lived, and how the business of a caricaturist was conducted in the late 18th and early 19th century. The issues of plagiarism and unwelcome competition are also explored in *The Military Caricaturist* (page 35).

Enjoy!   *Tony Rothwell - 2021*

Slippery Sam

There's an old pub in east London, Wapping actually, called The Prospect of Whitby, right on the banks of the Thames. If you're not from Wapping, you don't want to be wandering in there for a pot of ale and a pipe of tobacco, thinking you'll be safe. No sir! On the contrary, the local gentry will size you up and take appropriate action. This could range from ignoring you until you left, following you outside, knocking you on the head, robbing you blind and throwing you into the river; or sidling up to you at the bar all palsy-walsy and ending up kidnapping you for a ransom, if you were worth the trouble.

Not all Prospect regulars stayed on home turf for their livelihood though, not by a long chalk. One such was known as 'Slippery Sam'. An evil little man who had perfected the art of pickpocketing and had trained a local waif, name of Nick, as his accomplice for when they went 'up west' to places the nobs frequented - Bond Street, St. James's Street and Piccadilly, a favourite area because of the crowds and the shops. These people had money, were not in a rush and would look in the windows or stop to converse with acquaintances, making them prime targets.

One chilly day in early February 1808, with ice on the pavement, Slippery, a bit short of ready money, decided to see what pickings were to be had. For these escapades he would dress like a toff to fit in, complete with powdered wig, frock coat, knee britches, boots and cane while Nick would be got up like a poor, neglected orphan on whom the obviously-so-benevolent Slippery was taking pity. On this occasion Slippery even gave him a pair of skates so it looked like he was taking the lad out on the ice.

They had two main schemes. One was where Slippery would accidentally bump the target and lift anything of value, handing it quickly to Nick who would then make himself scarce while Slippery apologized profusely; the other was where Slippery took along something of value (usually stolen) telling the target it was surplus to requirements after a death in the family and might they be interested, at a bargain price. If the mark showed interest and started to ask questions, Nick would move in from behind and his light fingers would do the rest. They had become experts in their field, but rode their luck every time they went out. So far, they had never been caught.

After a couple of very successful picks in Piccadilly – a gold snuff box and several gold sovereigns for Slippery and a silver card case and silk handkerchiefs for Nick - they went on to St. James's, outside Hannah Humphrey's publishing business. There was always a crowd there looking at the prints in the window. A caricaturist called Gillray attracted people to the shop with his satires like bees to honey. Sometimes when a new one came out, often about the arch enemy Napoleon or even King George, people fought to get in the shop to be among the first to have it – a pickpocket's dream! On this occasion it was quieter but there were still a few citizens staring at the display in the window. Slippery had taken a barometer to "sell". Barometers were, after all, rare items. It had worked like a charm in Piccadilly.

But with Nick in place and Slippery making his move, disaster! Slippery's feet went from under him on the ice and, while saving himself with one hand and the barometer with the other, he hit the ground hard, spilling the sovereigns and snuff box from his britches.

With an uncharacteristic lack of judgment Slippery shouted "Quick, Nick, run," and off the boy scarpered, throwing the card case and handkerchiefs away, as he was trained to do. Unfortunately for Slippery this gave the game away, but he wasn't about to leave such rich pickings behind and tried to quickly grab them and run. That's when his luck finally gave out. As he rose, his feet went from under him again and he was eventually raised to the perpendicular by a large soldier who had been looking in the window.

And that was the ignominious end of Slippery Sam's pickpocketing career.

Historical Notes

This print, published on February 10th, 1808 was one of a series of six dealing with all types of weather.

As with the other thousand or so prints Gillray produced, he would have engraved the design on a copper plate. His publisher, Mrs. Hannah Humphrey, with whom he lived, then printed off copies which were hand-coloured by a team of women under the direction of Gillray, and sold in the shop. Amazing when you realize that this, and a thousand other plates he executed, all had to be engraved in reverse, including the writing. Sadly, he went mad in 1811, dying in 1815, but his influence on caricature lives on.

The Prospect of Whitby was so named in the 18th century when it was rebuilt after a fire destroyed the original 16th century pub. 'The Prospect' had been a cargo ship which moored there; Whitby is a coastal town in Yorkshire. You can still see the 500-year-old flagstone floor in the bar. Known by the locals as The Devil's Tavern, it was a popular venue for smugglers and was used as a base for thieves who stole from the ships coming and going on The Thames. The great English writer, Samuel Johnson, recommended that people go to Wapping, as the area had "such modes of life as few could imagine".

The penalty for adults caught pickpocketing was hanging. A child would have his hand burned.

I visited the pub in the seventies and was told by friends to be careful with my car. As I parked, a young cockney lad came up to me and said, "Watch your car, sir?"

"How much?" I said "Ten bob'll* cover it," he replied. I paid up, and when I came out, the car was fine. Relating the story later I was told that it would have been 'keyed' had I not parted with my money. Little had changed it seems, except extortion had replaced pickpocketing! I am assured it is now a totally safe place for a pint.

*ten bob = half a pound sterling, equivalent to approximately $7 today.

A Pair of POLISHED Gentlemen.

A Pair of Polished Gentlemen

as related by Arnold Smithwick, a London tavern storyteller.

"Growing up in the 1790's I had heard about Dick and Tom," said Arnold to a pipe-smoke filled room in The Bunch of Grapes in Blackfriars. You know the one, just up from Blackfriars Bridge on the Embankment.

"They were two of the most infamous 'young bucks' London had ever seen," he said. "There was always some tale about them circulating - their names might as well have been Mischief and Mayhem if half of what I heard was true." Then, lowering his voice and looking round the room, he almost whispered, "But just recently I was told a most curious tale which I think you will find of particular interest."

The drinkers put their pots of ale down and looked in. Arnold had a reputation for enthralling stories.

"Born into well-to-do families, living close to each other in Kensington, and bosom friends from a very young age," he went on, "they were seldom out of each other's company. Early on it seems, Dick read about blood brothers and with the aid of a knife they performed the ritual behind a stable, mixing blood from cuts on their arms.

They then set about the business of cheating, chatting and charming their way through their early years. As teenagers, they were in enough trouble and scrapes for 10 and often went too far, trying to outdo each other, causing distress and discomfort to many, much to their amusement, but somehow they came out smelling of roses more often than not. And there's no doubt the opposite sex was taken by their good looks, their dash, the life that was in them, and the possibility of romance that seemed to surround them like a halo. They broke quite a few hearts along the way.

That was until the day they went to the circus on Hampstead Heath. By that time they were, oh, must have been 20 I would say. They're in their thirties now but it was only the other day I heard this story. As most of you know I'm sure, the circus was always very popular, with the crowds flocking to see the exotic animals from Africa, the jugglers from France, the balancing acts from Italy and the clowns from anywhere and everywhere. But our two young bucks were not going to sit around watching the acts. They were there for a drink or two and to enjoy the sideshows and hopefully meet some pretty, young, unchaperoned ladies.

The story goes that after a couple of tipples they started moving along the sideshows, guffawing at the lady with the moustache, pretending to dance with the dancing bear, poking fun at the dwarf and, at the hoopla stand, one of them would distract the stall-holder while the other tried to lean over and put the hoop over a prize. They were soon shooed off and found themselves reading the sign on the next booth, more of a tent actually, which proclaimed -

Fortunata
The famous fortune teller and Mystic.
Find out what life has in store for YOU.
I'm Never Wrong!
One shilling to enter.

The two young gentlemen looked at each other, burst out laughing and agreed they just had to do it. Slightly tipsy, and full of their usual bravado, they weren't about to part with two shillings to some charlatan of a fortune-teller and agreed that they would somehow get away without paying – their usual modus operandi. They pushed open the tent flap and strode in. It was dark inside, the only light filtering through the canvas. Behind a small circular table, draped in a carpet and covered in weird objects and cards, was an old woman dressed in what looked like gypsy clothes, a tight red scarf tied round her head, and a few whiskers growing from her chin. Tom let out a snort when he saw her as he tried to stifle a laugh, which started Dick off giggling.

She ignored these outbursts and, in an accent somewhere in between mid-European and cockney, asked to see their money. Tom pulled out two shillings, but she told them she would only see them one at a time. "Can't go mixing up your fortunes now, can we?" she said.

They tossed a coin to see who would go first. Tom guessed right and decided to get it over with, so Dick left, shouting back over his shoulder, "Don't forget to tell him how many children he's going to have, altogether that is, with the bastards!" He thought that was hilarious and Tom could still hear him laughing outside.

He sat down and pushed the two-shilling pieces over the table. She put them behind a pack of tarot cards on the table and took his palm. She looked at it very closely and after a pause, and to his utter surprise, told him quite a lot about himself. It was as if she had known him for years. Then she picked up the tarot cards, fanned them out face down and told him to pick one. He picked a card.

The Hanged Man.

"Don't like hangings do ee, Tom? Not like all those Londoners going to Tyburn for their entertainment," she said.

"No," he replied, "hate them as a matter of fact."

"Well, you best be mending your ways, young Tom (how did she know his name?) or you may be the one they're gawping at one of these fine days."

Tom blanched and he suddenly went cold and goose-bumps jumped up on his arms.

Next, with closed eyes, she said she was looking into his future. After some rocking to and fro and some strange noises she pronounced that he had the chance to do good and be a kind man but finished by saying he would get himself into a very tight situation if he wasn't careful.

Tom went outside, in a mild state of shock, but he wasn't going to confess to Dick that she'd rattled him. He described the sequence of events and where the money was hidden and told him to wait until she closed her eyes, then grab the money and make a dash for it.

Dick went in and, sure enough, the pattern was repeated. She seemed to know Dick rather well too, and even mentioned some personal things only a member of his family would have known. She offered the tarot cards. He picked The Devil.

"Don't like the thought of hell, do you Dick? Worried that you don't go to church as regular as you should and make a clean breast of it – I'm right aren't I? And you thought that sign outside was just a come-on, to get people in. Well, you know different now don't you, you and your friend out there?"

Dick was mesmerized and when she closed her eyes to "look into the future" he forgot all about the money. He really wanted to know what she would say. She said he could lead a good life if he turned it around and helped others less fortunate than himself, but to watch out for a tight situation, which brought Dick round. That's exactly what she had said to Tom, he thought. She IS a charlatan.

He stood up, grabbed the money and ran out of the tent.

"Got it!" he shouted, "Come on, run!"

The evening was spent retelling their experience over some good port and insisting to each other that the fortune-teller had just made some lucky guesses – nothing to be concerned about – no reason for panic.

Next day Tom went round to Dick's house mid-morning as he did most days to discuss the plan for the day. But he had to admit he wasn't feeling very well. He had had a dreadful night, turning and tossing, waking in a sweat, the sheets all twisted about him. He had had terrible dreams, like none before.

He entered Dick's house via the rear entrance as usual. There was Dick slumped over the kitchen table, still in his nightshirt.

"What's the matter?" said Tom.

"I had a terrible night," he said. "Awful, awful dream. I dreamt we went to the circus, we had our fortunes told by that old woman. We picked ominous tarot cards - you The Devil, me The Hanged Man. And she warned us, something about getting into a tight situation and it was suddenly like I wasn't dreaming - it was real and my body was shrinking and I was all packed inside a riding boot and couldn't move. My arms were inside and you were next to me and you were in a boot too, only you looked happy and I was moaning to get out. My only thought was how am I ever going to eat, who's going to feed me? It was terrible. I thought I saw a hangman at the foot of the bed and I woke up in a cold sweat with the bedclothes trapping me, I thought I was going to die"... his voice trailed away.

By this time Dick was sitting bolt upright in his chair, his eyes wide, staring at Tom.

"You're not going to believe this, Tom, but I had exactly the same dream. I liked it at first. It seemed cosy in the boot I thought, but then it became a real nightmare. The Devil visited me, he really did, I swear, right in my room. He circled round the bed breathing fire, all scaly with red eyes and a pointed tail just like you see in drawings. I was terrified. That old witch must have put a curse on us. We should never have taken the money."

"Or laughed at her," said Tom.

Both were badly shaken. It was as though there were big weights inside them. They had never had matching dreams before, each one making the other so much more credible. But as lunchtime came and went, and the memory of it all had begun to fade, they started to get their old swagger back.

They had arranged to go riding in the afternoon and the groomsmen were to have their mounts ready at 2 o'clock. Tom and Dick went to their rooms and put on their riding habits. Last item was their boots. Tom pulled his on and felt something inside the right foot. He silently cursed his valet for his oversight. He took the boot off and turned it upside down.

A tarot card fell on to the floor.

Staring up at him was The Hanged Man.

At the same moment a few hundred yards away, another card was falling to the floor – The Devil.

Dick ran as fast as he could to Tom's house in hysterics. It was as if the devil were chasing him. He met Tom careering towards him. They took each other by the shoulders and stared into each other's eyes. They stood there silently for a moment, breathing hard and knew without saying anything that the other had also found a card.

That moment was the turning point in their lives they told me, ladies and gentlemen. What a turn-around and no mistake.

Dick started to go to church just as he knew he was supposed to. But now he wanted to. His life developed into one of service to others and he did much to turn young men away from meaningless, self-absorbed lives, to ones of purpose.

Tom, meanwhile, became a successful and much respected merchant, and made it his business to see to it that the poor in his area were fed and cared for.

And they have stayed good friends all these years.

Was there ever a Fortunata? Or tarot cards in boots? Tom and Dick insisted there were and that they kept the cards about their persons to ensure they stayed on the straight and narrow.

A couple of polished gentlemen after all. And that, ladies and gentlemen, is the end of my tale."

There were a few moments of silence, the audience looked at each other and broke into applause. Arnold had burnished his reputation.

Historical Notes

The print, published March 10th, 1801, features two inseparable members of London's fashionable set, Sir Lumley Skeffington and Montagu Mathew. The necessary tools for blacking and polishing boots surround them, insinuating that the principal polish of these two individuals was on their boots.

Pub.ᵈ Nov.ʳ 9ᵗʰ 1795. by H. Humphrey, Nᵒ 37. New Bond Street.

A DECENT STORY.

Letters Home from Venus and Mars

A letter to her parents from Miss Gwendolyn Cathcart   *November 10th, 1795*

Dearest Mama and Papa,

I trust you are well and that everything in the garden is blooming and fruiting down there in dear Tunbridge Wells.

I am sure you will be surprised to be receiving a letter from me enclosing a print engraved by that clever Mr. Gillray, delivered into my hands this very day.

As you will see I am in a happy frame of mind and that is not just because of the sherry wine but because, and here I beg you to take hold of something solid, I am become affianced, yes, engaged!

I know you had been thinking this event would never happen because, as you have frequently pointed out to me, Charles, my companion these many years, just didn't seem the marrying kind, and has steadfastly avoided any assignation where we would actually be on our own, let alone become engaged. But, *mirabile dictu*, it has happened and my heart is still racing!

How did this come about? You may well ask! Do you remember reading me bedtime stories as a little girl? You will recall that my favourite story was about Cinderella meeting her Prince Charming. I loved that story, but now I have a new favourite.

It all happened in a most extraordinary way. Those depicted with Charles and me in the print are friends from Monsieur Guillaume's Dancing Academy which you sent me to all those years ago. That, you will recall, is where I first met Charles and we had been gathering for soirées ever since, to which he has invariably escorted me. They are all happily married and, like me, have been unable to understand what could possibly be holding Charles back. A dashing, fearless soldier, a Major in His Majesty's Service, fighting the dastardly French on the Continent, sailing with his marines to all parts, staring down savage natives of every hue, sword in hand, he has singularly failed when it comes to matters of the heart and, in particular, *my* heart. This has been such a disappointment to me but, so it seems, it has to our friends who, bless them, conspired to do something about it, for hints were just not penetrating Charles' military pate. Unbeknownst to me they concocted a story, to be related at one of our evenings together. It seems Tom Arbuthnot, that most jovial of fellows, was chosen to be the story-teller on the appointed night, last Wednesday to be precise. He announced that it was called "A Decent Story" and proceeded as follows -

There was a gentleman, Rodney by name, approaching middle age, not yet married, who had a lady friend, Charlotte, whom he loved but could never admit it to himself or anyone else for that matter, while she was, in turn, pining away for him. Neither would declare their feelings for fear of being rebuffed, and so the relationship was withering on the vine like a bunch of wrinkled grapes.

(At this point I noticed a sharp intake of breath by Charles – I think it was the words 'grapes', 'wrinkled' and 'withering' following so hard on each other's heels).

Tom continued: One day Charlotte decided she had waited long enough and as they sat on a bench in St. James's Park one fine summer's evening she said "Rodney, don't you think it's high time we got married?"

Without thought Rodney replied with a sigh "Yes, my dear, but who at our time of life would have us?", with which Charlotte got up, glared at Rodney and said, "Well if that's the best you can offer, we will not be seeing each other again. Goodbye!" and she strode off without a backward glance.

Rodney realized what he had just said - truly the response of a habitual bachelor - and that he might never see his beloved again. Decisive action had to be taken – a flanking movement, a head-on assault – whatever it took. The story came to its conclusion with Rodney dashing after her and kneeling down in her path so that she had no alternative but to stop. His voice cracking with emotion, he said what a fool he had been all these years and asked if she would marry him. Charlotte half swooned, collected herself, threw her arms round him and shouted 'Yes! Yes!' And they lived happily ever after.

Tom announced that was the end of the story and around the table there were various comments - 'men do get set in their ways', and 'so an old dog can learn new tricks', 'a happy ending forsooth', that sort of thing.

At this point I carefully glanced under lowered lids at Charles who was looking ashen. But he caught my eye and his colour turned quite red. Then, stuttering just a trifle, he said the words I will never forget –

"He's not the only old fool, Gwendolyn. Would you consent to be my wife? I dare say we could make a go of it."

I was, of course, quite taken aback. Indeed, I was at a loss as to how to reply without appearing too keen, for my whole being wanted to cry out, but something stopped me. Was I making him suffer a little for my long wait? I could see that our friends were holding their breath in great expectation of my answer but I calmly took a sip of sherry, looked slowly at each of them in turn and finally at Charles and said, "I will, Charles, but the marriage had better take place this year while we can still make it down the aisle without assistance!"

General laughter and rejoicing then ensued as our friends congratulated us most heartily, and then each other, for their ruse had worked more effectively than they had dared to hope.

I will be bringing Charles down this weekend in the Saturday post chaise for him to ask you, Papa, for my hand and to discuss arrangements. Please consent! He is assuming that you will approve of a military marriage with guard of honour, crossed swords *et cetera*. Won't it be splendid?

Can you believe that your daughter is finally engaged to be married? I can't quite believe it myself and, but for the story, I don't think I ever would be. Three huzzahs for the storytellers say I.

Your affectionate daughter

Gwendolyn

A letter to his parents from Major Charles Fortescue

November 12th, 1795

Revered Parents

I write to inform you of my forthcoming marriage to a Miss Gwendolyn Cathcart. Known her for some time. Nice gal. Good family. I shall keep you abreast of plans. How's the gout, Father?

Yours ever

Charles

The print was published on November 6th, 1795. The only contemporary explanation of it was "It needs no explanation."

MATERNAL LOVE.

The Fashionable Mamma, — or — The Convenience of Modern Dress. Vide The Pocket Hole &c.

The Tardy Viscountess

*L*ord Frederick Croker was a climber. A social climber that is. He had inherited a baronetcy from his deceased well-to-do father, Charles Croker, but every bone in Frederick's body, every hair on his head, detested his position as a baron, the lowest order of the nobility. Yes, he had inherited money and land, but not the title he felt appropriate to his station. A baron! Demeaning, unacceptable. He needed to ingratiate himself with those who could raise his position in London society, to be seen in the best circles, invited to the most sought-after events, to exchange pleasantries with the Prince of Wales – now *that* would be something – and eventually obtain a position which would guarantee a higher rank. A plan had to be put in place, starting with marriage!

Frederick had inherited the Croker genes – tall, boyish good looks, but short of body and long of leg. Generations of tailors had wrestled with this discrepancy - the Crokers insisted on presenting themselves well, both in the salon, and the saddle – and after one or two damp squibs, he managed to land a well-connected wife, Cecilia. She too was tall and thin, with an elongated nose giving her a somewhat imperious air, but they made a handsome pair. Through her, Frederick was immediately vaulted into a more promising social strata and for her part, she knew full well why he had sought her out. But the marriage suited her too because she had attained the age when there might be a question mark hovering over her, were she not married. And she had to admit she rather enjoyed being addressed as Viscountess.

The invitations to the best soirées and desirable dinners came thick and fast to the newly married couple, but Frederick was impatient for success, especially since it wasn't long before he became a father. Now he wanted a worthy title, not only for himself, but to pass on to his son and heir when he shuffled off this mortal coil.

There was, however, a fly in the ointment. Cecilia found it impossible to be on time for anything, let alone important social engagements. Unfortunately for Frederick she was, at least for the moment, the primary invitee and so her husband had to mind the reproaches which seethed within him as they arrived late as usual, when many of the personages he hoped to buttonhole had moved on to other events, being much in demand by the upper crust of London's social round.

Showing a modicum of constraint, Frederick would scold Cecilia pointing out that being late was impolite, but she would return his rejoinders with interest such as "You may be right Frederick, but it has been my experience that those who are late enjoy life far more than those who wait".

And so there were no changes in the Croker household.

The birth of the child had only made matters worse. The recent writings of Jean-Jacques Rousseau had convinced ladies of the value, to both mother and infant, of dispensing with the wet-nurse and accepting the responsibility of breastfeeding themselves. Cecilia had taken this to heart, so now there was a baby to be fed on top of the hours long *toilette* she seemed incapable of shortening.

One particular evening, m'Lord was at the end of his tether after arriving even later than usual at a highly fashionable *avant-guarde* event, owing to the feeding before dressing. But what was this? His eye was drawn to a lady wearing a dress which unashamedly allowed glimpses of her breasts, as the flimsy material fluttered about her upper body.

He quietly pointed out the dress to Cecilia who told him that she was well aware of the new fashion, which had recently made the journey over the Channel. His Lordship quickly came to the conclusion that at least an hour, perhaps even more, could be saved by his wife taking to this latest thing from France.

It was a turning point in their marriage and, as it turned out, in Frederick's climb up the social ladder. Cecilia had thought her husband would be either too shocked or too pompous to allow her to adopt such a provocative fashion but, *au contraire*, he encouraged it. The effect was that she suddenly seemed very keen to be on time and was only too happy for her husband to be off saying all the right things to the right people, while she, thus unencumbered, was able to flirt.

By the time the boy was one, Lord Frederick had succeeded beyond his wildest dreams in his aspirations for social elevation. He had been made Earl of Framlingham, appointed Master of the Horse to King George, and a Privy Counsellor to boot, while Cecilia had that glow, and love of life, which accompanies only the most ardent attention from the opposite sex.

Now, more often than not, it was Cecilia who was first in the coach.

Historical Notes

'Lord' is the title barons are permitted to use, while the wife of a baron may use the title viscountess.

The waiting coach and Cecilia's chair are decorated with a baron's coronet. We can only wonder if her husband was already inside it, drumming his fingers.

Master of the Horse is a largely symbolic position in the Royal Household with a most spectacular dress uniform. It would have been a challenge for Lord Croker's tailor. A Privy Counsellor is a distinguished person who advises the sovereign.

The Prince of Wales would become the Prince Regent in 1811, on the perceived madness of his father, King George III, and would accede to the throne as George IV some 11 years later. He was a charming man with beautiful manners and a keen interest in the arts and architecture. However, there was another, more dominant side to him, and he died in 1830 after a dissolute life of multiple affairs, drunkeness and gambling.

London, Publish'd November 20th 1804, by H. Humphrey, No 27, St James's Street.

— B. Esq: del. —

— FORTUNE-HUNTING. —

18

Fortune Hunting

Lord Blenkinsop was a good man. Good family. Acquaintance of the King. Wide of girth. Not the sharpest knife. Took his responsibilities seriously though, always had.

One of them being the further education of his nephew, Nigel Carruthers.

When he was 19, Nigel's courageous Royal Naval father, Captain William Carruthers had been killed by a musket ball on his poop deck while serving His Majesty on the sloop HMS Orion, fighting the French off Brest. "Damn that little shrimp Boney and his dastardly ambitions," muttered His Lordship at Carruthers' funeral as the service wore on and on. And that is when, in an instant, he decided that it was his solemn duty, *in loco parentis* so to speak, to make sure Nigel was schooled in the ways of the world. With no children of his own, he had always taken an interest in the boy who he felt had lived a rather sheltered life, father always away on the high seas and tutors coming to the London house throughout his childhood. And more recently, fencing and dancing instructors if you please. The result was that he had few friends of his own age with whom to get out and about.

When Blenkers (as Lord B was affectionately known in the family) put the idea to his sister-in-law, Marjorie Carruthers, she agreed wholeheartedly – the tutoring had been her husband's idea and had severely restricted her social life as it required her to be at home rather than out with the fashionable set to which she felt she belonged, a ruse of the oft-absent Captain. But now that her husband had departed this world, Blenkinsop's notion suited her down to the ground – she needed to see and be seen in society, even if her attire was, temporarily, mourning black.

His Lordship planned an agenda for the proper instruction of a young man entering London society. To start, he took him to his club where he had his first proper taste of alcohol, a brandy no less, reading The Times in a large leather armchair after a good lunch – quite the gentleman about town. On another day they went to a coffee shop, a place of male intrigue if ever there was one, concluded Nigel – it appealed to him a great deal and he entered into some interesting conversations. On another, it was off to the House of Commons, where shouting down the current speaker seemed to be the order of the day, but where again he took a keen interest in the proceedings. In the evenings they visited a tavern or two where Nigel evinced quite a deal of attention from the ladies, unused to seeing young men in their teens in city inns. The longer this "education" went on the more Nigel seemed to be enjoying it. He was getting a taste for ale and brandy and His Lordship was very pleased with the way the programme was proceeding, and with the boy's keen interest and sharp mind. "Blossoming, if you ask me," reported

Blenkinsop to Marjorie Carruthers, "like a bottle long-stoppered, finally released!" She'd noticed the change, too, and was all for it – the more he was his own man, the more freedom she would have.

Next it was to be the country, for they were 'cits' and if you were a cit it was fashionable to spend time getting back to your roots by going out to the country - riding, hunting and mixing with the country folk. "Salt of the earth," Lord B proclaimed to Nigel, "not used to the ways of London, but happy with their lot. Hearts of oak, don't you know. They'd give you the shirt off their back. I'll take you out as my groomsman and show you the ropes."

On the appointed day for their country excursion Lord B hired a post chaise which took them, already regaled in their equine garb, to Sarratt in Hertfordshire to The Boot Inn where decent hunting horses were to be had by the day for a few shillings. The vicar of Sarratt was an old acquaintance of His Lordship and had spoken glowingly of the countryside around the village. They looked quite a pair – Lord Blenkinsop being, let us say, corpulent, and dressed in traditional hunting clothes straining at the seams, while Nigel was as thin as a rake and attired in a baggy blue groom's coat and wide-brimmed hat. Not exactly the country squires they hoped to be taken for.

They duly arrived at The Boot, ordered two horses to be saddled and after a pint of ale and some bread and cheese, mounted up. Using a rough map the landlord had prepared for them with a recommended route, they made their way past the church until they were able to break off into the fields and copses.

They spent the next hour or so pretending to be huntsmen, shouting "tally-ho", chasing after imaginary foxes and wishing they had guns whenever a pheasant got up in front of them. Following the map, they eventually started to head back to the village when the horses suddenly set back their ears and made off at a good gallop for a stand of trees in the distance. In spite of our heroes' best attempts to slow them down, the horses kept to their course and, before long, arrived among the trees where they came to a halt in a clearing. The would-be huntsmen, who couldn't understand what had got into the horses, dismounted to get their breath back. As they did so an old lady and a good-looking young wench, both dressed in ragged clothes, emerged from the trees and started to feed apples to the horses.

As they did so, the old lady spoke: "What you be doin' 'ere, sur?

"If you must know we're just out from London, taking the air and getting a little exercise," said Blenkinsop rather testily, unused as he was to be questioned by someone dressed in rags.

"You be trespassin' on those 'orses, sur" said the old lady. "This be crown land, belongin' to the King you understan', only folks on foot 'ave roight o' way 'cross it."

"Oh dear," said His Lordship, now looking distinctly flushed.

"But we don't 'ave to report it to no-one under certain circumstances," the old lady continued, half closing one eye and raising a crooked finger to make her point.

"And what would those circumstances be?" asked Lord B.

"Well, let me see now," said the old lady "How about you press some silver into my palm and I'll tell your fortune, and Mary there will tell your young friend's and we need never say nothing more 'bout it?"

"I suppose that would be alright," said Blenkinsop, softening, as he had no desire to do anything that would put him in bad odour with His Majesty. "How much?"

"Let's see," said the old crone, "I think a couple o' guineas should cover the situation."

"Two guineas!" exclaimed Blenkinsop as his face turned red. "That's highway robbery, ma'am, and you know it!"

"Do I? Do I now?" said she. "Well suit yerself. We'll just 'ave to report yer then, won't we?"

"That won't be necessary," said His Lordship, who knew from a lifetime of experience when he was on the losing end of a bargain, "but these fortunes better be good."

During this exchange Nigel had been ogling the young wench who had gained his complete attention. She was the comeliest girl he had ever seen, and she was also showing an interest in him. Unfortunately for our heroes they had not noticed that, while thus distracted, a third gypsy was hanging down from a tree and rifling through the portmanteau on the back of Blenkinsop's horse while a fourth was expertly picking his pockets.

Meanwhile the old lady held out her hand to Lord B who reluctantly took out the necessary coinage from his waistcoat pocket. She carefully counted the money and told the wench (Mary, she called her) to get started.

The young girl took Nigel's hand. "That's an intrestin' palm if ever oi saw 'un," said she. "Let's see now. Yer'll 'av a long loif sur, 'an yer'll be lucky in luv an' be blessed wi' many healthy chillen. That's all oi see there."

"Is that IT?" exclaimed Lord B with incredulity. "That's about a shilling a word! Is that the best you can do?"

The old lady chimed in, "If oi were' you sur, I'd remember wot oi said about trespassin' on the King's land an' count moiself wery lucky. Now let's see yer palm."

Lord B turned away from her and said to his nephew, "Come on Nigel, I'm not waiting to hear what rot they have to say about me," he said, resigned to having been taken advantage of, "Let's leave these witches and get back to the inn and wash the taste of them out of our mouths."

"Wery noice sentiments oi must say," said the old lady. "Be off wi' yer then an' take more care where yer go nex' toim."

The horses, it seemed, had had their fill of apples and were content to take their riders back to the The Boot, with Nigel occasionally looking back to see if he could get a last glimpse of the girl – he could still feel her hand holding his, but she had disappeared. They arrived at the tavern and looked for the landlord to tell him what had happened, but he was nowhere to be seen. They told the coachman to load their belongings into the post chaise and stand guard, ordered their ale from a serving girl and fumed over their expensive experience. After a while they began to relax, deciding to order another ale "for the road", and Lord B finally saw the funny side of their outing when Nigel reminded him of his statement about country folk giving them the shirts from their backs.

"More like we lost our shirts," guffawed Lord B, a typical Blenkers attempt at humour. "Time to go. Your mother will be wondering what's happened to us."

"I'll need to relieve myself for the journey first, Uncle," said Nigel.

"Off you go then, I'll see you in the coach."

Nigel made his way across the inn's courtyard and round behind the stables to the privy. As he was standing there, he heard muffled voices next door. In disbelief he thought he recognized the old lady's scratchy voice. Could it be, he thought, and leant closer to the wall.

"Oh yes, we took 'em proper" she was saying. "You trained them 'orses well, Jim – came straight to us didn't they, Mary? They luv them apples! Two guineas in my palm and Billy 'ere got two pocket watches with chains and our Sal got a couple o' silk 'kerchiefs. 'Ere's yer share and good luck to the lot o' us!"

By this time Nigel had crept round the front of the building and grabbed a pitchfork leaning up against the wall. He threw open the door, shouting, "Caught you red-handed, you scoundrels. You're not getting away with this. Do you know that's Lord Blenkinsop you just robbed, a confidante of the King himself, whose name you just took in vain out there in the woods – probably a hanging offence!"

With which he leveled the pitchfork at the landlord's throat and held it as though it was a rapier and said, "Put all the money and the watches in the handkerchiefs, tie them up and hand them over." He made a jab with the pitchfork to show he meant business. The landlord flinched and, with trembling fingers, did as he was told. He had gone as white as a sheet, while the women just stood there, their mouths gaping open.

"Now the next part is up to you," Nigel said, looking at them one by one. "We can either have a constable come out here and have you all arrested and locked up, if you're not hung that is. Or you can solemnly swear that you will discontinue this loathsome practice here and now."

This statement was greeted with silence other than the sound of the old lady wringing her hands and moaning and the landlord's knees knocking. "Very well, I shall call my uncle and he will take the matter over."

"No, no, no, no need for that" said the landlord, looking at the others who nodded vehemently in agreement. They knew the penalties for what they were doing, and it sounded like they were going to be given a second chance. "That won't be necessary, young sir. We were misguided. Very misguided. We'll stop today, 'ere and now, we swear. On the 'oly Bible. Don't we, ladies?"

"Yes. Yes," they said, out of dry throats.

"Very well," said Nigel. "But to make sure you do, Lord Blenkinsop will write a letter to his friend the vicar here and tell him what has transpired today, that you have sworn to stop your thievery. However, if he hears anything to the contrary, he is to contact us, and we will put the wheels in motion for you all to be arrested. Goodbye to you and I hope never to see your faces again."

One last look at the girl, who didn't know whether to be impressed or furious, and he was gone and climbing into the coach. Seconds later they were out of the courtyard and on the road back to London when his Lordship asked, "do you usually take so long to relieve yourself, my boy?"

Nigel's reply was to ask him to open his hands. "Playing a game, are we?" Lord B enquired.

"You'll see, Uncle," said Nigel, with which he pulled out the handkerchiefs from his pocket and untied them.

"Good lord," said his uncle, "there's my watch, and yours, and my money! How did you get them?"

Nigel recounted the whole story to an astonished member of the peerage. He wasn't sure if Nigel had made the right decision about letting them off so lightly, but he was impressed with his nephew's quick thinking and courageous action.

"Your father would have been very proud of you, as am I," he said. "Swift, decisive action. Definitely a chip off the old Carruthers' block!"

"And to think I was taken with that girl back there," said Nigel, shaking his head.

"A part of your education I hadn't reckoned on, I must say," replied Lord B with a wry smile.

The post chaise eventually arrived back at the Carruthers residence after a most interesting and, as it turned out, exciting day.

"Do we tell your mother?" asked His Lordship.

"Let's just tell her we've had a good day fortune hunting, eh Uncle? What's on the agenda for tomorrow?"

Historical Notes

The print was published on November 20th, 1804, from a sketch by Brownlow North.

Captain Carruthers would have been on blockade duty off Brest, intended to stop French ships getting in or out of harbour. It was long and tedious duty but every now and again one or more ships would make a break for it and if they were spotted, a sea battle would ensue.

Both the French and the English employed snipers with muskets in the top rigging to shoot officers with the objective of weakening the resolve and organization of the opposing force.

Scientific Researches! — New Discoveries in PNEUMATICKS! — or — an Experimental Lecture on the Powers of Air

The Wager

*I*t was one of those most singularly enjoyable evenings with my good friend Sir Benjamin Thompson, now Count Rumford - politician, *bon viveur*, principal founder of the Royal Institution and inventor of the famous Rumford Stove (no well-equipped house in London would be without one). Your writer is Freddy Thoelden, a London merchant of some means, who had assisted Sir Benjamin in the distribution of his stoves to all parts, making a tidy sum while doing so, I must confess.

We met at White's, our club in St James's, the headquarters of the Tory party and much beloved by sporting types, in this case those who like to bet, rather than sweat.

The food had been wholesome if not extraordinary, but the club claret had flowed - I believe we consumed three bottles - God bless those froggies – can't stand them but what would we do without their wine? Throughout the evening, however, I had the impression that the good Count was leading up to something. And so it proved, as we waded in to some excellent port, for he suddenly announced, apropos of nothing - "Freddy dear boy, I'll wager you one hundred guineas that within 30 days from today you will witness fire and smoke emerging from Sir John Hippisley's fundamental orifice!"

His words were slurred and his attempt at 'fundamental orifice' was particularly amusing, and I was forced to ask him to repeat himself as I was not sure that I could possibly have heard him right. Repeat it he did, and seemed completely in earnest! A hundred guineas indeed! Our wagers were usually more in the order of five pounds.

In any case, I took the wager and shook hands upon it, knowing that he was in his cups and tended to make these eccentric wagers late in the afternoon, usually for effect. Indeed, they were often not even remembered the following day and, if that were the case on this occasion, I had every intention of letting him out of it, as I had done once before, after sobriety had replaced bravado. But when we met at our usual coffee house in Fleet Street the very next day, he not only remembered making the bet, he positively refused to have any part in foregoing it.

"No sir," he said with a conviction I had not before witnessed. "A bet laid is a bet played - a hundred guineas we said, did we not? There's no going back, unless of course YOU want to wriggle off the hook. Hmm? You're looking surprised, my dear Freddy – getting cold feet?"

"Not I," I replied somewhat weakly. My membership of White's would certainly be brought into question, were I to renege on a wager, but I have to confess I began to wonder anew what on earth could have possessed the man to make it.

"Very well then," he said, "let's keep this one private, between ourselves shall we?" and off he tottered.

A hundred guineas being not an inconsiderable sum, and my meeting with Rumford having discommoded me somewhat, I decided that a conversation with Sir John H would be prudent. Knowing him to be a man of habit who regularly exercised his horse in Rotten Row of an afternoon, I found myself in that vicinity on my nag the very next day, and soon spotted Sir John on his chestnut coming towards me.

"What ho, Sir John," I cried with a cheery smile as we approached each other, "mind if I drop in alongside?" "Good afternoon Mr. Thoelden, er yes, I suppose so," was his surprised reply. I wheeled my horse round and, as I was now a few feet behind him, I had an excellent opportunity to examine his posterior from which, I was pleased to note, neither flame nor smoke were currently emitting.

"How is your health, Sir John?" I chirped as I drew alongside.

"Never better," he replied quizzically. "Why this sudden interest in my well-being?"

"Oh I dunno," I replied "I heard that you might be under the weather a bit – just wanted to be sure that all was well – no bowel problems, things of that sort."

"Bowel problems! Is someone going around saying I have bowel problems?" He looked and sounded decidedly peeved.

"No, no I'm sure they're not, just a figure of speech you might say. Glad to see you in prime health, sir. You look very fit. Obviously, you know the importance of minding your diet, keeping the intestinals clear, that sort of thing. Jolly good show. Must be off now."

With which I turned away and with a final look back at his rear for further reassurance, I trotted off, leaving Sir John no doubt somewhat perplexed. But at least I was satisfied that the wager was almost certainly safe - he looked very well. Fire and smoke indeed! I then dropped the matter, feeling even more certain I would soon be pocketing the hundred guineas.

The next two weeks were taken up with the usual round of London's social occasions, and I quite forgot about the wager until a messenger arrived at the door with a heavily embossed invitation from the Count to attend a scientific lecture and demonstration at The Royal Institution.

As I read the invitation a cold chill shot through my body as I realised that the date of the lecture was within the 30 days I had agreed for the wager. Could there be a connection? I made a note to call on the Institution and enquire as to the nature of the planned demonstration.

The following day found me trolling down Albemarle Street and rapping on the Institution's massive door which was opened by none other than Sir John himself. I was baffled by his presence there and stuttered something along the lines of how nice it was to see him again. He coolly asked my business, and when I said I was interested in the forthcoming lecture he bade me enter the vestibule where he briefly left me, returning shortly with a Mr. Thomas Young who, according to the invitation, would be delivering the very lecture to which I was invited. Sir John introduced us and then left, affording me another chance to glance in the direction of his rear – still untrammelled by the slightest trace of combustion.

I told Mr. Young I was just passing and, as I was planning to come to see the demonstration, thought I'd pop in, at which he kindly asked whether I would like to see the room reserved for such occasions. I replied in the affirmative and into the lecture theatre we went. A most unusual scene met my eye - a stout desk-like table surrounded by two rows of padded benches, with cupboards crammed with multifarious scientific equipment of the most advanced and complex design. The whole area was lit by my friend Rumford's latest lighting invention, his Astral Lamps, with shades of the finest gauze, giving off a most luminescent light. And then it came to me that Rumford had mentioned that Sir John had taken the position of Manager of the Institution and had assisted with the installation of his lamps. Feeling a little relieved I asked Mr. Young what was involved in the stated title of the lecture 'Pneumatics'. Mr. Young replied that air in all its forms and uses would be discussed, but for the life of me I could see absolutely no connection with the wager.

I thanked Mr. Young for the tour and told him I looked forward to an interesting evening, though I have to confess that the subject filled me with little enthusiasm. But, as we went back into the vestibule and made towards the door, he said something which caused me to experience that chill again – "You know you must be the ninth or tenth person who has visited the Institution over the last two days asking about the lecture," he said. "I cannot understand why – we've never had this degree of interest in advance of a lecture before. It's as though people were expecting we had just found the cure for the common cold or invented a flying machine! Most curious. In any case, we will see you on the day, Mr. Thoelden" he murmured, and with that he bade me farewell, leaving me to ponder what I had just heard.

My sensibilities were now so very much heightened that I decided my next visit would be to Count Rumford's residence in Smith Square to see if I could find out why he was so sure in his bet. But, on arrival, I was told by his housekeeper that he was away at his country seat and would not return until the evening of the lecture. This did nothing to assuage the increasingly large knot in my stomach, but I resigned myself to having to wait it out, telling myself over and over again that I had seen Sir John twice in the last few days and on both occasions he had seemed in fine fettle.

Eventually the day of the lecture came around. Having taken a light supper without so much as a glass of sack - I needed my senses to be at their very sharpest - I made my way to the Institution and occupied a place in the lecture theatre opposite the aristocracy, as was the custom, I was informed. I looked across the room and there indeed were my Lords Gower, Stanhope and Pomfret, Sir Henry Englefield and, giving me cause for concern, Sir John Hippisley. On my side of the room were William Sotheby, the poet; Peter Denys, the painter (Denys is an artist and associate of that disreputable caricaturist Gillray); and there were several to my left I did not recognize, including ladies of quality. My seat was at the left of the table, affording me an excellent view of the proceedings, as I was able to look down its entire length.

A latecomer was Isaac Disraeli, the essayist, no doubt delayed by his pen, while the last person to enter was Count Rumford himself. He took his place at the opposite end of the table to myself, but stayed on his feet. I was aware that those around me were looking at him with a curious mixture of expressions, ranging from anticipation to excitement. Meanwhile he bowed slightly from the waist, as in turn he caught the eye of each person present with that knowing smile with which I was all too familiar, for it usually meant he was in confident mood. His eyes eventually fell on mine and, though I could not be absolutely sure, I thought I detected the slightest wink of his right eye, but at that point Mr. Young entered the lecture theatre to polite applause, followed by a young man with a thicket of brown hair.

Rumford welcomed everyone to the Institution and told us that tonight's subject was, as we knew, pneumatics and that Mr. Young would be assisted in the demonstrations by the up-and-coming scientist and inventor Humphrey Davy (he of the hair).

And so we started. What was air? Of what was it made up? He surprised everyone by informing us that oxygen made up only 21% of air, while nitrogen, which we simply exhale, contributed the majority. He went on to say how fortunate we were to have air around us, as life was unsustainable without it. It delivered essential oxygen to our blood, and possibly no other planet in the universe but ours possessed it.

As wind, it delivered ships to our shores and made commerce possible. It gave us the world's best navy and indeed the audience might like to know that an Englishman, Mr. Robert Fulton, had just recently demonstrated that a vessel which trapped air could submerge under the waves – a submarine he called it – and attack our enemies unseen. The first of its kind in the world. (Some gave a rousing huzzah at this news of English invention and power which woke others from their slumber, as Young's delivery was not of the most scintillating variety.)

Air, he continued, drove windmills that ground our flour, it sustained the animals we ate, it literally fuelled our lives. Without it fire was not possible, as fire needed oxygen to burn and where would we be without fire? And, if that were not enough, it had the capability of being compressed by means of bellows to start and sustain fire, which Davy demonstrated.

At these mentions of fire, I felt decidedly discomforted and I glanced in Rumford's direction for any sign, but he continued to look straight ahead, wearing the same contented expression, while Sir John Hippisley's visage maintained a benign smile.

Young went on to show how air in its compressed state could be used in various contrivances to propel mechanisms useful to the good of mankind. He concluded by reminding us how vital compressed air was to music, from organs to bagpipes. "It would be a dull world indeed without music to entertain us," he opined. Almost as dull as his delivery, I thought to myself, but I had to admit that I felt a new kinship with air and its properties and more importantly, I was very relieved to see that Sir John's only involvement in the proceedings had been to help with the equipment, though he did smoke his pipe from time to time. However, what smoke there was, was firmly confined to his frontal, rather than his anal, orifice.

During my musings Mr. Young was finishing his presentation, bowing low, and was afforded a round of applause. But as this died down Rumford stepped forward and announced there was to be an additional demonstration – a little something he had planned with Mr. Davy, who stood behind Young with rather a silly grin on his face, still clutching his bellows.

"My apologies, Mr. Young," Davy said, "this was a last-minute addition Count Rumford wished to include, and you were not here this afternoon when he arrived from the country. I will need the services of Sir John and yourself, if you please. The demonstration involves the unusual effects of laughing gas on the human voice and I have here the necessary equipment," putting down a retort on the table which he had retrieved from one of the equipment cupboards. Young had heard about this curious effect, though it didn't seem to fall under the heading of pneumatics, but he did as he was requested.

Davy took charge of the proceedings asking Sir John if he would be the guinea pig, positioning him at the end of the table, directly in front of myself. I began to get a very uneasy feeling. Davy then came forward with his bellows and asked Sir John to take the tip of the funnel into his mouth when he would have the first of two gaseous substances blown under pressure into his mouth, which Sir John should inhale.

Sir John looked a little concerned but did as he was instructed, Davy brought the two sides of the bellows together, blowing the gas into his mouth, then, stepping away, asked Young to put the retort into Sir John's mouth and clamp his nose with his other hand. This struck Young as odd but he executed the move. "Inhale," said Davy.

Then it happened!

There was a thunderous explosion from Sir John's hindquarters, flames shot out of his britches followed by smoke. I looked on aghast, concerned both for Sir John's health and for my pocket, as I realized that I had been well and truly taken. Those of us nearest to him rushed to Sir John's aid. Not surprisingly he was in a state of shock. Meanwhile all around there were cries of "for shame" directed at Rumford.

Sir John was carefully laid on the floor, his head propped up. Brandy was brought and administered, which seemed to calm and revive him wonderfully. Having been informed by Davy that there was no lasting harm done to his person and that he indeed had inhaled laughing gas, he immediately confirmed this by commencing to giggle, to the great relief of all present.

As this was happening, I began to reflect on the recent occurrences – the fact Rumford had asked to keep the wager secret, that others had been to the Institution enquiring about the lecture in advance and his sudden disappearance to the country and now the cries of "for shame" - and I realized that possibly everyone in the room had taken Rumford's wager without any of us knowing it! Just as I was coming to this conclusion Isaac Disraeli stepped forward looking very fierce and confronted the Count, demanding an explanation, saying he was damned if he was handing over a hundred guineas to anyone, least of all Count Rumford, "clearly the perpetrator of this chicanery".

Count Rumford put his hand up and asked for a moment of silence to explain.

"My lords, ladies and gentlemen, I admit I have presumed upon your good nature," he started "but I can assure you that it was with the best of intentions. You have all heard tonight's lecture, one in a series we give every year, GIVE being the operative word. We are now three years old and making great progress in the field of scientific discovery, but the means to sustain the Institution are sadly depleted. This little ruse of mine was a way of raising enough money for us to keep going long enough to establish patents on our inventions so that we can become self-sustaining."

"So why didn't you just tell us that?" demanded Disraeli. Others murmured in support.

"I did!" said Rumford. "As you may remember, I approached all of you and many more, several months ago but you told me you were being taxed to death to pay for the war with Boney and could not afford a sous, so I had to put my thinking cap on and decided to approach all my friends who appreciated a wager. You are all acquainted with the rest of the story, but if any of you do not want to see it through, I will gladly let you out of your obligation and say no more about it. I'm sure I can count on everyone's discretion to keep the matter within these walls?"

We looked at each other in astonishment.

"Well, I for one think it was a damnably clever idea," said Lord Pomfret, the most senior member of the peerage present. "I made a bet and I lost – so be it. Here's my hundred guineas. Put it to good use is all I ask of you, and long may the Institution prosper and thrive."

Given this pronouncement and given the pronouncer, there was little anyone else could say. True, there were a few grumbles here and there, but it would have been a reckless person to go back on a gentleman's handshake and, in the end, everyone parted with their money.

I understand that the Institution was the better off by as much as one thousand five hundred guineas as a result of the Count's ingenious plan to winkle the money out of us, which he had concocted after talking to Davy about his experiments with laughing gas, or as he calls it, Nitrous something-or-other. Sir John recovered quickly, and one of the first uses of the monetary influx was to replace his britches, but I dare say he will not be volunteering for future demonstrations.

You could say the evening was no laughing matter - but I'm sure you wouldn't.

Historical Notes

The Royal Institution* was founded in 1799 and exists to this day. Count Rumford was the principal founder of the Institution and did invent the Rumford Stove and Astral Lamps.

Apparently, the print was sent to him while in Paris by Sir Joseph Banks, President of the Royal Society, and in a letter of thanks Rumford wrote "...the Gillray print you sent me has afforded me much amusement".

All of those named in the story are real and were identified contemporaneously. My story is, of course, a complete fabrication, yet much of it has roots in fact:

- White's Club still exists today and was originally a chocolate house, being founded in1693 by Francesco Bianco (Frank White!). Chocolate was a very valuable commodity in those times thus the houses attracted the well-to-do and many converted to fashionable gentlemen's clubs over the years. White's became the unofficial Tory Party headquarters (as Brooks was that of the Whigs) and had a well-earned reputation for the eccentric bets made there, including one in 1816 when Lord Alvanley bet a friend 3,000 pounds, a fortune in those days, as to which of two raindrops would reach the bottom of a window pane first.

- Fulton's first submarine had in fact just been successfully tested in Brest Harbour (see notebook on the padded seat behind Lord Pomfret).

The Institution was indeed in financial decline at the time of this print but continues to give lectures – perhaps the money came just in time!

*The Royal Institution's purpose was set out as: "The diffusing of knowledge and facilitating the general introduction of useful mechanical inventions and improvements; and for teaching, by course of philosophical lectures and experiments, the application of science to the common purposes of life."

Caricature Wars

An extract from *The Times* of December 8th, 1799

The MILITARY CARICATURIST.

"_his Satires are as keen as the Back of a Rasor; — and having but Three Ideas in the World,
"Two of them are borrowd, — & the Third, nobody else would own_." —

IT IS REPORTED THAT THE LATEST BROADSIDE FROM THE PEN OF JAMES GILLRAY is aimed not at those frequently targeted – the Prince of Wales, Napoleon, or some unfortunate member of high society – but at a fellow caricaturist! It seems that Thomas Davies, a Lieutenant General in the Artillery no less, and a self-proclaimed caricaturist, had spoken ill of Gillray. This was, perhaps, not well advised. It has given rise to a typically ferocious response from Gillray this week in the form of a print entitled *The Military Caricaturist*. It depicts a pathetic-looking soldier, pen in mouth, with hunched shoulders and sword dragging on the ground. Behind him are excruciating examples of Davies' supposed work, such as a young woman presenting her bottom to be kissed entitled *Wit*, and a grotesquely fat nude female entitled *Grace*. Also to be found in the print is a bulging folio of work by rival caricaturists, suggesting plagiarism.

A sub-caption to the title is equally devastating – '...his satires are as keen as the Back of a Rasor; and having but Three Ideas in the World, Two of them are borrowed, & the Third, nobody else would own.'

Perhaps the clue to this third idea can also be found in the print. On a table lies *Aretino's Postures*, a guidebook of sexual positions; *La Pucelle*, a poem by Voltaire notorious for its sexual content; and a bottle labeled Velno, an apothecary remedy for venereal disease.

Our conclusion? Think twice before crossing Mr. Gillray.

Publish'd November 20.ᵗʰ 1804 by H Humphrey N.º 27 St James's Street London

_ An Old Maid on a Journey. _

36

The Superiority of Sophia Sarah Banks

Sophia Sarah Banks was a lady of uncertain age who had an opinion on everything ("and I'm right, you'll see" she always ended her tirades). While her famous brother, Sir Joseph, was off round the world on his endless search for botanical specimens ("bits of fungus" was her term for them) she herself was a noted collector of ephemera and prints, driving a hard bargain when on the scent of something she wanted. Not that she really needed them, more that she wanted to deny them to anyone else – such was her nature, a strong desire to be superior. When not turning London upside down for her "treasures" she ruled the roost at the family household with choice cuss-words and a sour expression, neither of which you wanted to be in the way.

A large woman with a wobbly chin and singularly small feet, she barged about like a ship in full sail, particularly when mounted on her man-sized horse, Thunderer. Most days she galloped across the fields of neighbouring farms with no regard for livestock or crops, wearing one of her three riding habits which, bizarrely, she called Hitum, Titum and Scrub. The farmers had long since given up trying to make her stay to the roads and bridle paths ("there's no challenge in going where everyone else goes" she told them). When not riding she was accompanied everywhere by her pet lapdog, Marmaduke, which followed her round the estate or was otherwise carried under her ample arm.

Sophia Sarah had two servants, both male, ("can't stand whimpering women") who loathed her superior ways but were too scared to hand in their notice. There was Mulgrave, part butler, part cook, whose major pre-occupation on his own time was drinking, as his grog-blossomed nose bore witness, and Donkin, a simpleton, who did the rest – cleaning, polishing, gardening and looking after the horse and her song-bird. He was a whistler was Donkin as he went about his tasks, something he did subconsciously, which was his most common state of being.

The problem for the village was that Sophia Sarah always needed to win. When the local parson, the Rev. Cedric Finnerty ("he's a fool, that one") announced in church that the village was going to hold a Bring-and-Buy sale in answer to the call from the Prime Minister, William Pitt, she sensed an opportunity. The country needed to raise money to help the war effort against Boney and the French ("they don't wash you know") and she decided that her wares would be "superior". But what was she to take? She didn't want to give up any of her treasures. She decided to make something, an original – she would show them who could come up with the best goods ("just like I always do").

She started to consider embroidery. The one and only concession she made to femininity was that at the end of a long day of riding, cussing, and complaining, she liked to relax with a port and lemon and get out the embroidery. That's it, she thought – I'll surprise them all with the excellence of my cross-stitch and the beauty of my design.

And so she started in on the work, buying many different coloured threads and a handsome frame to create a superior foot-rest, sure to sell well among the gouty inhabitants of the mansions thereabouts.

The sale was to be in the local hostelry "The Cock in Britches" in two months' time, and the whole village would be there with their wares. What's more there was to be a free drink and muffin for everyone who came, courtesy of the landlord, and music was to be provided by a military band. The sale was also announced from the pulpits of all the local churches to ensure a good turn out from the surrounding area and everyone got into the spirit. It was one way those not fighting Napoleon on land or sea could get involved, and the more they made from the sale they thought, the less likely it would be that Pitt would think of some new tax on poor old John Bull* to pay for this expensive war.

But Ms. Banks had other priorities. Not for her the satisfaction of merely making something saleable and donating the proceeds to the cause – she had to WIN. She wasn't sure what she wanted to win but she would soon arrive at that. So, as she sat sipping her port, she thought how she could come out of the sale in superior fashion. Then suddenly it came to her - there would be a judging, that's it, a judging of all the wares before the sale, which would mean that her piece, which would obviously win first place, would then go on to command an even higher price. Brilliant, she thought, as she drained her glass with a self-satisfied smile.

It all needed to be arranged, so she went to see that fool of a parson and told him what she required to happen. He was clearly not happy, but she browbeat him, even told him her substantial tithe was in jeopardy, and so finally, being totally dependent on pledges for his livelihood, he reluctantly agreed to make the announcement in church.

Sunday came round and the sermon was duly delivered, at the end of which the Reverend mentioned the competitive element that had been introduced to the sale of wares, and gave a half-hearted explanation of how the best items would then fetch more money. There was a murmuring among the congregation but Ms. Banks, sitting in the family pew, had that self-satisfied look on her face again as she contemplated a further, and very public, example of her superiority.

Many of the villagers went straight to the Cock in Britches (the 'C in B' the locals called it) after the service and started to talk about this latest development. They soon found that no-one liked the idea, and some said they might not make or take anything if that was the case, as they didn't want to be shown up. After a fair quantity of beer had been consumed, Bill, the landlord, was deputed to approach the parson and see if the idea could be overturned.

That Monday morning Bill duly went to see him and told him of the villagers' feelings about the sale being "turned into a ruddy competition, wi' judges an' the like". Finnerty said it certainly wasn't his idea, but that only led to Bill demanding to know where it had come from. The parson could not avoid the question and as soon as the name was revealed Bill understood what was going on. He thanked the Reverend and went back to the pub to get ready for opening time.

As the locals filed in, Bill quickly spread the news, which was greeted with a good deal of anger. "That woman has got to be taught a lesson," said one old-timer into his ale, seemingly expressing the thoughts of many, judging by the comments.

And so, the locals set about concocting a plan which they hoped would bring Ms. Banks down a peg or two.

The following Sunday Ms. Banks decided that it was far too nice a day to go to church and went riding instead. She wore Scrub.

Some weeks later, on a fine November Saturday morning, an hour after Ms. Banks had set off in the post chaise to London in search of more treasures, the villagers went down to the C in B with their wares and laid them out on tables in The Ram, the hostelry's dining room. They were soon encouraged by the arrival of large crowds of eager beavers from villages all around, looking for something interesting or tasty to buy. Judges were nowhere to be seen.

The day went by quickly with Bill and his wife Marge doing a roaring trade, the band playing patriotic music, and locals and visitors alike enjoying a unique day in the village's life. At noon there was a visit from the local Member of Parliament, Sir Archibald Fitzroy and a heroic naval captain, awaiting his new warship to be completed. Between them they made grand speeches about England's duty, the villagers' loyalty and the visitors' generosity, which seemed to make sure that everything was sold and a handsome sum collected. Bill and Marge produced free hot toddies and muffins for the journey home, and everyone declared it an excellent day indeed.

Precisely one week later Sophie Sarah Banks made her way to the C in B clutching her parasol and her fan ("they'll make a good impression on the judges don't you think?") with Marmaduke under her arm, followed by her entourage – Mulgrave carrying the now-finished embroidery and Donkin whistling along behind with the song-bird in its cage, which Ms. Banks thought would attract more people to examine her fine work. Bill and Marge greeted them with a wan smile and a Bill of Fare, pretending that they must be there for a meal, and ushered them towards The Ram.

"Where is everyone?" demanded Ms. Banks.

"It's a bit early yet for the locals," said Bill.

"I know that. For the sale and the judging I mean!" exclaimed Ms. Banks.

"That were last week ma'am," said Bill, keeping as even a tone as he could manage, "didn't yer know? It were announced in church".

"It CAN'T have been! I distinctly remember it was the eighth."

"That were changed to the first, said Bill. "T'were announced in church - p'raps you missed it. What a shame."

"This can't be happening - I've slaved over this embroidery - it would have won..." moaned Ms. Banks leaning against the wall for support, her voice trailing off.

"Ne'r mind ma'am, the sale went very well and everyone 'ad a grand time. Made lots of money for Pitt's lot. We even 'ad Sir Archibald 'ere giving a speech."

"Sir Archibald! I've always wanted to meet Sir Archibald. This is a CALAMITY," she cried.

"I'll tell yer wot" said Bill in a friendly tone. "Why don't yer leave the embroidery 'ere at the ol' C in B an' we'll auction it off for yer on a night there's a good crowd in - nex' Saturday should do it."

"Leave it here, among the ruffians of the village and their foul-smelling pipes - you must be mad!" shot back Ms. Banks.

"Well, that's the best I can do for yer," said Bill, "and it'll be the only thing for sale - pride 'o place, yer might say."

Sophia Sarah's chest heaved, her face was red, she stared at Bill, still extremely put out. Mulgrave and Donkin took a sudden interest in their boots. She had been riding one Sunday, she finally remembered – she must have missed the announcement. Suddenly she seemed to sag and, for once, seemed almost resigned to something not having gone completely her way.

"Do you think it would sell well?" she asked at length.

"Let's 'ave a look at it" said Bill. "Marge, ye'r a good judge o' stitchin' an' such', what d'yer think?"

Mulgrave presented it for inspection. It really was fine work.

"It's luverly" she exclaimed – "with Christmas round the corner it'll make som'un a very fine present."

And so it was that the foot-stool hung over the bar for a week for everyone to inspect. On the Saturday, with the pub bulging with locals, including Ms. Banks sipping a port and lemon "on the 'ouse", Bill conducted a brisk auction, with Sophia Sarah's item eventually being knocked down to a slightly over-generous bid from none other that the Rev. Cedric Finnerty, who mumbled something about wanting it for his wife (a guilty conscience for his part in the deception no doubt).

But Ms. Banks thought that perhaps he wasn't quite such a fool after all, indeed clearly he was a man of taste, and she gave him her best winning smile, a rare sight indeed, when the auction ended.

For their part, the locals made her very welcome, taken aback to see her in the pub at all, let alone subject herself to the possible embarrassment of her work going to a low bid. The whole night was a turning point in her relations with the village - especially as she enjoyed herself so much that she bought everyone a drink!

In the weeks and months that followed, she still occasionally put on airs - old habits die hard - but even Mulgrave told his drinking chums at the C in B, "you could say her superiority has lost a little of its lustre."

Historical Notes

The print, "An Old Maid on a Journey", was published on November 20th, 1804. Little is known about it.

Dr. Dorothy George, author of The British Museum's Catalogue of Political and Personal Satires, says in her description of the image that it is "traditionally" believed that the central figure is Sophia Sarah Banks, so even that is not certain, but what lies behind the scene depicted in the print, where it takes place and who the other people depicted are, is not known or even guessed at (until now).

What we do know for certain is that Sir Joseph Banks did have a sister called Sophia Sarah; that she did collect prints and ephemera including caricatures, among them Gillrays (it is a nice thought to believe that she might have actually possessed this particular print); that on her death she had amassed such a collection that her sister-in-law, Lady Banks, was able to donate over 19,000 items to the British Museum and British Library; and that she did indeed have three riding habits named Hitum, Titum and Scrub!

All the rest of the story is fiction – or is it? Just look at that face!

*John Bull is the British equivalent of Uncle Sam.

The Suitable Suitors

(and a dancing bear)

Ever since Sir Richard's untimely death from a sudden stroke there had been an increasing number of enquiries of Lady Fiona as to how she was bearing up, did she need company, that sort of thing. They were kindly, of course, but taking stock of those making the solicitations it became clear that, while they had initially come from her relatives and lady friends, they were now beginning to emanate from gentlemen - single gentlemen. Indeed, when her period of mourning was over, it wasn't long before the enquiries became invitations. And Fiona, who had at first consoled herself solely in the company of her faithful dog, Jack, found herself seriously considering the opportunities with which she was now being presented.

Fiona was someone who loved life, but also someone who had not had what might be called a joyful marriage. It was true Richard had given her a title, a son (currently a soldier waging war against Napoleon in Europe), two well-found houses, one in the country, the other in the city, expensive jewellery and the latest clothes, but little by way of affection, or even attention. He was always off with his friends or seeking influence among the aristocracy, leaving her to her own devices. To him she had been little more than an ornament, brought out when the occasion required.

But Fiona was not one to sit at home and wait to be 'required'. More and more she found amusement in the soireés of the likes of Georgiana, Duchess of Devonshire and other members of the smart set in London – a group of aristocratic ladies who dressed in the height of fashion, wore the most exotic, bejeweled and befeathered wigs and gambled and drank away their husbands' fortunes in a life close to dissipation. In addition, she had taken a cicisbeo*, who accompanied her to parties and other society events. Her choice had been a most willing and amusing rake - but she gave him up when Richard died. What was she to do now?

She consulted an old friend and confidante who told her in no uncertain terms - "You, my dear, are what all men seek – good-looking, humorous, well-preserved and well-off. Now that you have no ties, it's high time you made a *tour d'horizon*, to see what, or rather who, might be available. And you never know, you may find a true soulmate even yet."

And so, over the next few months, Fiona had a remarkably full diary, accepting many of the invitations that came her way. But eventually her more persistent suitors, of whom there were five, started to press their case for a more permanent arrangement, along with remarks designed to run down their competition whenever the opportunity arose. This took all the enjoyment out of the situation for Fiona and she realized something had to be done.

One rare evening when she found herself at home with nothing in her diary, she sat down with Jack on her lap to decide on a plan of action. As was her custom, she talked to him as though he were a person - he was, after all, very intelligent - and commenced by describing each of the suitors. Jack was all ears.

"First there's Gilbert Blunt. A divorcee; rotund, gouty, but a man with something very definitely in his favour – he farms half of Buckinghamshire! The trouble is I always view divorcees as potentially faulty goods, but I have to say his gifts are very generous.

Then there's Andrew Duncannon. He's a bachelor and a barrister. Not sure why he has become one of my favourites as he tends to be rather quiet, but he helped me greatly with Richard's affairs when I needed it. And just when you least expect it, he utters a witticism or droll remark which never fails to make me smile. And his pronouncements of affection seem very sincere.

Next there's Sir Edward Ponsonby. A retired Major. He is by far the most handsome of the five and I dare say we make a good-looking couple when I am on his arm, no doubt like many a lady before me. He is a bit of a braggard though, constantly regaling me with tales of his derring-do in battle. When he retired, he bought himself a seat in Parliament and is an up-and-comer in Pitt's Tory Party. He does well on his political connections and service pension, or so he keeps telling me.

Number four is Spencer Blanchard, a lonely widower if ever there was one. A man who has devoted himself to public service, and is currently an Alderman of the City and widely thought to be a future Lord Mayor of London. So, what do you think Jack? How would you like your mistress to be Lady Mayoress of London - rather grand, don't you think?

And lastly there's Neville Carlisle, a bachelor and a fat one at that! He's an Oxford don, highly intellectual and obviously lives very well. He dazzles me with his understanding of just about everything, but does he talk! He's really not my type, but I find it very difficult to say no to him. It's as though it would somehow reflect badly on my judgment if I did so. Perhaps I fear what he would say of me, but he can be quite sweet when he's not being brilliant.

So, there they are, Jack – my five suitors."

Jack looked at her, his head cocked to one side in a questioning sort of way. "I suppose you want to know my favourite? Well, if I had to choose now, I would put Sir Edward in the first position and possibly Andrew Duncannon the second, but it's very difficult – they are all suitable in their own way."

As she looked down at Jack an idea began to take shape. Yes, that was it. She would arrange a tea-party at home and invite them all, but in such a way that they would think that they were the only one being invited. For good measure she decided on April 1st as the date. She'd often had fun on April Fool's Day so why not? She didn't know what would happen, but she felt something would come of it, and if nothing else, it would be very amusing. She had the invitations delivered the very next day.

Lady Fiona Holland

invites you to take tea with her

on April 1st. at four o'clock in the afternoon

to discuss matters of mutual interest.

R.S.V.P.

The invitations might as well have been fireworks for the explosive effect they had on the recipients. Each knew that this was it! What else could there be to discuss but their betrothal? Five affirmative replies flew back.

Gilbert Blunt started thinking about an expensive ring, "diamonds and rubies I think" he mused. Major Ponsonby rehearsed a speech as though he were about to address parliament, or was it his troops? Alderman Spencer Blanchard envisioned a grand reception in Guildhall with the Lord Mayor in attendance, and Neville Carlisle started to get excited about the coming joys of the wedding night.

Only Andrew Duncannon had doubts. It certainly sounded like there was a real chance for him, but after a few minutes of quiet reflection he had convinced himself that Fiona needed more advice on her late husband's affairs. Yes, that was it, how silly of him to get ahead of himself like that.

Over the next two weeks Lady Fiona turned down all invitations and left the suitors to their own devices. Of course they were out and about and, when occasionally they saw each other, they seemed to be overflowing with bonhomie as they put on their best 'I know something you don't know' smiles, or passed each other with a cheery wave as much as to say – 'you don't know it yet, dear boy, but you have lost the prize'. Andrew Duncannon was very perplexed and was once on the point of asking Blunt why everyone seemed so friendly all of a sudden, but he decided to keep his thoughts to himself.

The day finally came around and the five suitors converged on Lady Fiona's London residence - three on foot, Carlisle and Blunt in carriages, and all dressed in their very best town clothes and wigs impeccably powdered, except for Duncannon who was damned if he was going to pay the guinea tax imposed lately on powder**.

But what was this? One by one they saw their competitors making for Fiona's residence. They tried to remember the wording of the invitation. Perhaps they had misunderstood. No, they couldn't have – it was very plain. Had they been tricked? No, Fiona wouldn't do such a thing. Nothing for it but to go through with it. Meanwhile Duncannon was wondering about the complete and very sudden disappearance of the bonhomie so recently displayed. No-one spoke a word. They just glowered at each other, feeling confused, uncomfortable and very put-out.

Carlisle was nearest the door and rang the bell. The door was opened by the butler and there in the foyer stood Lady Fiona, dressed in the latest Paris fashion, a long flowing dress of saffron-colored silk with matching hat, complete with feather. She smiled broadly at each one as she invited them in. Carlisle, who was determined to be the first to kiss the hand of the hostess, advanced, but so did Blunt at exactly the same time. The result was that the two of them got stuck in the door which only served to emphasize their considerable girths. After a swallowed curse, Blunt gave way. The afternoon was not getting off to a good start for Buckinghamshire or Oxford.

The rest followed into the foyer and Fiona led the way into her most elegantly appointed dining room. As a husband, Richard had been rather dull, but he had money and he allowed Fiona to spend it. In front of them was a table covered in beautiful china and platters of various tea-time comestibles, surrounded by six chairs. A painting over the fireplace of Cupid, complete with bow and arrows, caught Ponsonby's eye and set his heart racing.

Now, where were they to sit? There were no place cards.

All of them of course wanted to sit next to Fiona but while they were making their moves, it was Duncannon who stepped forward to hold a seat out for her which immediately made the others seethe - an opportunity missed! Carlisle and Ponsonby immediately grabbed the seats on either side of her. Duncannon moved her chair in, and as the others sat down, he found the only seat left was behind a giant urn.

Lady Fiona bade them welcome, thanked them for coming and invited them to help themselves to tea, but it was not only muffins but also the atmosphere that could be cut with a knife. No-one was making conversation. They looked a bit like children at their first birthday party. Suddenly it seemed, all these *gentlemen* didn't know how to behave. Fiona, ever the hostess and not insensitive to the situation, broke the ice saying how mild the weather had been and where were those April showers? Upon which Carlisle began a long treatise on trends in temperatures he had been studying for the last 20 years and "don't you know each year we are experiencing lower average temperatures," at which Blunt interrupted saying that's what must be affecting the yield from his thousands of acres of wheat, while Ponsonby interjected that farmers were asking far too much of the government in this time of war, as he was remarking to the Prime Minister only the other day, when Blanchard cut in with a statement that essential food costs were out of control in London and what he wanted to know was, what was Pitt proposing to do about *that*?

At this point manners completely went out of the window with everyone barking over and at each other as though Fiona wasn't even present. She filled her lungs and bellowed "WOULD ANYONE CARE FOR SOME RUM AND WALNUT CAKE?"

The room instantly fell silent except for Carlisle, who was still droning on about his temperature theories. But the others piped up with 'Oh yes', 'absolutely', 'indeed good lady', 'if you please', 'just a small piece perhaps', 'delicious tea', they chorused, suddenly embarrassed by their show of ill-manners.

At that, Fiona got up out of her chair and made towards the bellpull to summon the cake.

This was a signal for each of them to raise themselves out of their chairs and hurry to render her a service – no lady should be pulling bellpulls when there were five gentlemen present. As each did so, he realized that he was not the only one with the same thought and the matter then took on the form of a race to the bell – with disastrous results. Blunt fell, having tripped over Ponsonby's foot, Spencer shot up and somehow impaled Blunt's wig on his knife causing Carlisle to poke a muffin into his eye while Ponsonby, who had trodden on Jack's paw, let out an ear-splitting howl as the dog sunk his teeth into the major's knee. Meanwhile china and cutlery, muffins and eggs, were scattering in all directions, the teapot went flying and the urn was overturned. The gallant suitors then realized that they were, in any case, too late to assist Fiona, as one last china cup fell to the floor with an expensive crash.

Quiet descended on the room, broken in turn by a whimper from Ponsonby, a curse from Carlisle, an apology from Blanchard and an unfortunate noise from Blunt. Duncannon meanwhile picked up the urn and put its lid back on.

The cook and a maid, hearing the cacophony, came running in - the cook carrying the rather delicious-looking rum and walnut cake, while the maid started to clear up the debris. At this point the gentlemen realized the best thing for them to do

Company shocked at a Lady getting up to Ring the Bell.

London, Publish'd November 29th 1804 by H Humphrey, N 27, St James's Street.

B. ⊕ Esqr del.

was retreat and enjoin the battle for Fiona's hand on another occasion. They moved towards the door muttering 'so sorry, have to go Fiona', 'appointment in the City', 'vote in the House', 'need attention for my eye', 'my knee' and so on. Fiona, suppressing a smile, thanked them for coming, tried to apologize to Ponsonby for Jack's behaviour, and said goodbye as she watched their backs disappear into the foyer. Only Andrew Duncannon stayed to help clear up the devastation.

When they had brought the room to some sort of order, Fiona offered him a piece of the rum and walnut cake. "At least that didn't perish in the fray," she said. "Did you ever see such a thing, Andrew – will they ever forgive me? Will *you* ever forgive me? But it was funny, don't you think? What will they say? I know I got you all here under false pretences, but I had no idea Armageddon would ensue, even though it is April Fool's Day! Thank you so much for staying and clearing up, you are a dear and you seem to be the only one who came away unscathed."

"It's the least I could do, Fiona, and if I may say so, it was the most entertaining thing I've seen since I witnessed a dancing bear, wearing a skirt, walking down Regent Street juggling coconuts."

Fiona looked at him quizzically for a second, then realized what he had said, and broke out into peels of laughter, finally releasing the emotions bottled up over the last few months, not to mention the tea-time debacle. "Andrew, you say the funniest things. You're the only one who can make me laugh and I do love to laugh. I'm beginning to think you could steal my heart."

"Really, Fiona, do you mean it? *I'd* walk down Regent Street wearing a skirt and juggling coconuts if you really did."

"That won't be necessary, Andrew – just come here and give me a kiss."

Historical Notes

The print that inspired the story – "Company shocked at a lady getting up to Ring the Bell", was published on November 20th, 1804.

Smallpox was a terrible scourge in the 18th century, killing 3 out of every 10 who contracted it. However, an English physician, Edward Jenner, developed the world's first vaccine in 1796 and began successfully vaccinating people against the disease. Presumably Sir Richard either decided not to be vaccinated or was too late.

The derivation of the word 'vaccination' comes from the latin word for cow – vacca. Cowpox was a milder form of smallpox and it was noticed that cow farmers were immune to smallpox.

* In 18th century England convention accepted that ladies who had given their husbands a son and heir could take a cicisbeo (Italian for platonic lover) who provided sexual services and escorted them to events their husbands would not be attending, as long as the relationship did not interfere with their marriage.

** The Prime Minister of the day, William Pitt, imposed many taxes during this period to help pay for the expensive war against Napoleon. The names of the gentry who paid the guinea tax on powder for wigs were listed on a notice at their local church and they became known as 'guinea pigs'- the origin of the phrase we use to this day.

Bears were first introduced to Europe in the Middle Ages and proved to be a popular sideshow entertainment in countries where bears were not indigenous. There is no evidence of one being seen in Regent Street juggling coconuts, but we can dream.

The Plumb-pudding in danger

CPSIA information can be obtained
at www.ICGtesting.com
Printed in the USA
BVHW062208110122
625983BV00009B/1098